first experiences

Going to nursery

This book belongs to...

· ·

first experiences

Going to nursery

Written by Jillian Harker

Illustrated by Michelle White

Bright ☆ Sparks

It was Monday morning.
Jodie opened her eyes
when she heard Mum
coming up the stairs.

"Time to get up!" Mum
called, as she put her
head round the door.

"Don't you want to go and
see the nursery?"

"Yes, I do!" Jodie said.
She wanted to find out more
about the nursery that Mum
had talked so much about.

Jodie jumped out of bed and Mum helped
her to get dressed.

"Mum?" said Jodie. "What's it like at nursery?"

"Do you like climbing–frames?" Mum asked her.

"Yes, I do!" said Jodie.

"Then you'll like nursery," Mum said. "There are lots of exciting things, like climbing – frames, to play on. Come on, let's hurry up and then you can see for yourself."

Dad was waiting for Jodie in the kitchen.

"All ready to look at the nursery?" he said.

"What's it like there, Dad?" replied Jodie.

"Well, do you like painting pictures?" asked her dad.

"You know I do!" laughed Jodie.

"Then, I think you'll love nursery," Dad told her.
"There are lots of interesting things like that to do."

Jodie ate her cereal and her toast.

"I'm ready!" she cried. "Let's go!"

When they arrived at the nursery, a lady was waiting to meet them.

"You must be Jodie," she said, smiling. "I'm Mrs Clark. Would you like to see what we do here?" Jodie nodded.

Mrs Clark opened a door into a big room full of children having fun. Some of them were playing on a yellow climbing-frame.

Some of
them were
digging in
the sand – tray,
with buckets
and spades.

One boy was
painting a picture
with bright paints.

"Mum," said Jodie,
"you were right.
There are *lots* of
exciting things to
do at nursery."

Soon, it was time to go, but Jodie had *so* many questions about nursery. "When do I start?" she asked, on the way home.

"Next week," said Mum.

While she was eating lunch, Jodie said, "How long will I stay there?"

"Just for the morning, to start with," replied Dad.

Watching television
with Mum that afternoon, Jodie asked,
"Can I take teddy with me to nursery?"

"Of course," smiled Mum. "I think he'll enjoy it."

Next morning, Jodie and
Mum went to the park.

As Jodie was climbing up the slide,
she met a small boy, who was standing at the top.

The little boy's mum smiled at Jodie's mum.
"He's starting at nursery next week," she said.

"So am I!" cried Jodie.
"What's your name?" she asked the boy.

"Jack!" he said, whooshing
down the slide. "Do you
like nursery?"

"I think so," Jodie told him.

"I'll see you there," said Jack
and he ran off, waving.

The week quickly passed and at last, the day came for Jodie to start nursery. She was very excited and a little bit scared, all at the same time.

"Where am I going to put my coat?" she asked Mum, as they pushed open the door of the nursery.

"They'll have your very own place ready for you," said Mum.

"Hello again, Jodie," said Mrs Clark. "Can you see the hook for your coat? It's the one with the blue pig. Now, what would you like to do first?"

Jodie noticed a boy, who was working on a big puzzle of a fire engine. It was Jack.

"Hi, Jack," she said. "Can I help?" She picked up a piece of puzzle and fitted it into place.

"I think it's time for me to go," whispered Mum, giving Jodie a hug.

"Okay, Mum," Jodie smiled. "See you later," and she picked up another piece of puzzle.

"Jodie's really good at this, isn't she?" said Mrs Clark to Jack.

Jack nodded – it was fun at nursery.

When the puzzle was finished, Jack said,
"Let's go and play with the water – tray now."

There were buckets and funnels and bottles and
boats. They poured and dipped, scooped and
dripped. Then, Mrs Clark came over to ask Jodie
and Jack if they would like to help pass round the
drinks and apple slices.

"Oh yes, please," they said, together.

"Everyone, come and meet our new friends,"
said Mrs Clark. All the girls and boys came over
to say, 'Hello'. Then, Mrs Clark asked Jodie and
Jack what they would like to do next.

Jodie knew exactly what she wanted to do! She tugged Jack over to the dressing-up box.

"Look," she said, pulling out two hats, "we could be firemen!"

Jack pointed to a big, red car, standing in the corner.

"And that could be our fire engine," he said.

After Jodie and Jack had put out lots of pretend fires, they ran over to the climbing–frame. Jodie put her teddy at the top.

"Someone needs rescuing!" she cried and off she went up the climbing–frame, with Jack close behind!

From the top of the climbing–frame, Jodie saw two girls, busy making things at a table.

"That looks fun," she told Jack. "Let's go and see."

They ran over to the table. There were boxes and cardboard tubes and glue and paint everywhere!

"Let's make a fire engine," said Jodie.

Jodie started to glue two boxes together. She cut some card circles for wheels and Jack helped her stick them on. Then, they painted the whole thing bright red.

They were just about finished, when Mrs Clark called out, "Story time!"

Mrs Clark asked if Jodie would like to choose the story. Then, Jodie sat on a big cushion, to listen.

Just as the story finished, Jodie's mum slipped in through the door.

Jodie ran over to her.

"Come and see," she said, dragging Mum over to the modelling table. "We made a fire engine."

"It's lovely!" smiled Mum. "Shall we take it home with us? It's time for lunch now."

Jodie put on her coat and waved to Jack.

"Did you have a good time?" asked Mum.
"Do you want to come again?"

"Yes, I do!" cried Jodie. "Nursery is *great* fun."

This is a Bright Sparks Book
First published in 2002
BRIGHT SPARKS, Queen Street House,
4 Queen Street, Bath BA1 1HE, UK

Copyright © PARRAGON 2002

Created and produced by THE COMPLETE WORKS

ISBN 1-84250-540-8

Printed in China